JASON LUTES

Jar of Fools

BLACK EYE
PRODUCTIONS

ACKNOWLEDGEMENTS | This book is respectfully dedicated to Rachel Bers, Edwin Brubaker, Abigail Gross, Thomas Hart, Robert Jazz, Megan Kelso, Benjamin Leff, Jon Lewis, Scott McCloud, Howard Rigberg, Allison Schwartz, James Sturm, Michel Vrána, Chris Ware, and Deborah Zeidenberg, who collectively provided the inspiration and support necessary to its completion.

Jar of Fools originally appeared in serialized form in the Seattle, Washington Stranger and the Providence, Rhode Island Nicepaper.

The Al Flosso depicted in Jar of Fools is based on the real Al Flosso in name and likeness only, and is in no other way meant to represent him.

BLACK EYE PRODUCTIONS, PUBLISHER
338 Kribs Street, Cambridge, Ontario Canada N3C 3J3

ISBN 0-9698874-3-4

Publication design
by Jason Lutes and Michel Vrána

Printed and bound in Canada

Jar of Fools

PART TWO

But Dad fools 'em! I mean, you're wearing a tuxedo! People are going to *expect* tricks out of you!

That's true, that's an important part of it.

They know, and they give in. It's a little surrender. A moment of belief.

In what?

I don't know, *anything*. Anything other than what they know, or what they think they know.

That's the magic. Not the trick itself, but what it makes possible in people.

Or what it *used* to make possible, anyway.

Hey, there it is.

 What, it's an aquarium?

 No, silly, it's that door.

 But there's no sign.

 Through the door, down some stairs. Believe me, it's there.

 I don't know, I don't... it'd be weird if I just went in...

 Look, your brother's not down there or anything. Dad just got the suit there.

 Jacket.

Huh?

 Not suit. It's a straitjacket.

 Uh huh. Okay. Yeah. Just go in, will ya?

 I'll wait.

Good morning to you.

Uh... 'morning.

Just looking, or is there something in particular I can help you with?

Actually, um, someone I know bought some things from you a while ago...

an escape artist's gear? A straitjacket, and an iron ball and chain with cuffs?

This person, this man who 'bought' these things, he is a friend of yours?

Uh oh...

No, no, actually, no. I heard about it through a third party.

I don't know the man personally, I just heard about it. What I need is to find out where you got those things.

5

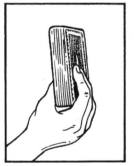

...but all I had to bargain with was an old shell deck Al gave me a long time ago.

What'd you get for it?

It's not much to go on...

I'll say. No address or anything?

MORTON E. CRANE

No, but that's the name of the guy who pawned Howard's stuff...

and I rec—

!

Uh... Claire, let's ... let's cut up here, okay?

Okay.

Doesn't make any difference.

How do you think Dad and Al are getting along?

7

Isn't there some sorta limit t'this abuse?

Hey, fuck *you*, Charlie!

Screwin' people over the way that you do!

Hey, I don't screw anybody, okay? Everybody walks away happy.

Cock-a-roaches got more dignity'n *con*-men!

Dignity? Take a look at yourself, will ya?

Talkin' t' *me.*

That's right: *talkin',* not *lyin'.* There's a difference.

Right, old man. Like you're line a work ain't built entirely on deception.

Hey, people pay t'see a trick, they *know* it's a trick.

I give 'em what they want.

Yeah? Me too. Chance t'help a guy with a flat, chance t'help a nice deaf man...!

I make 'em feel like they done some good in the world.

You lie to 'em.

Call it what you want!

But y'know, sometimes? They *don't want the truth!*

15

Hey, hey! She's gotta practice a long time before she shows anyone a trick!

I think it'd be okay, Al.

Months, years I'd practice before goin' public with a trick!

Public? Who's public?

Should I do the Ace one, Ernie?

"The Reappearing Ace." Yeah, that's your best one so far.

Pop!

Here's the deck.

Okay.

Only, I'm gonna do it with a Queen. I want it to be "The Reappearing Queen."

Uh, are you sure about that, Claire?

Ha ha! Lookit her, goin' off on her own already!

I'm sure.

Here, Dad. "Pick a card, any card."

Now put it back anywhere you want.

Okay, take the card underneath the one you just put back, and it is...?

The Queen of Hearts? The Queen of Hearts.

Yeah, kinda detracts, knowin' the name of the trick, doesn't it?

I'm not done yet, Dad. Put the Queen back into the deck.

19

Thank you.

Okay, now watch carefully...

I'll deal them out one at a time; keep your eyes peeled for that Queen.

Hey! That was it!

POP!

AAH!

Aw, pumpkin...!

It's okay!

Just a little slip, is all.

You'll get better. We'll get a new deck tomorrow.

You gotta be shittin' me.

'Night, Ernie.
'Night, Al.

Good night,
Claire.

So?
What do you
think?

I can't decide whether
you're a better teacher'n me
or she's a better
student'n you.

She's good, all right.
I just don't see how
that's gonna help.

I mean, you an' I
both know it ain't
a magician's world
anymore.

Unless you're
David fucking Copperfield,
making the Eiffel Tower
disappear on T.V....

Real subtle,
that guy.

He was all over the
T.V. back at the home.
People couldn't get
enough of 'im...

21

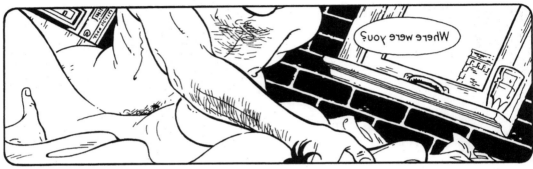

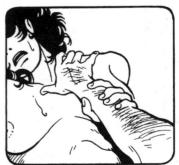

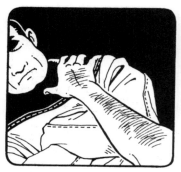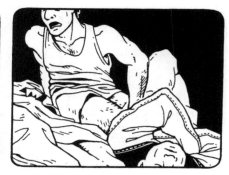

Hey, Ernesto.

Got any matches?

Psst! Hey.

Oh, uh... Mr. Lender, this is Esther. Esther, this is Nathan Lender.

Well, well; charmed, I'm sure.

You really *are* some kinda magician, eh, Ernesto?

I'm afraid we're all out of matches.

Okay.

I'm goin' out t'clean up, rustle up some supplies. Look after Claire?

Uh huh.

See ya soon.

Good morning, ma'am. Gotta light?

Sorry.

Hey, buddy...

'Scuse me! You gotta light?

So how does...

He shared yer pain, y'know? It helps spread it out a little.

I mean, *I* know what it's like, too. Who doesn't? Sure, the details may vary...

but the basic feeling, it's the same. It's the same in each an' every one of us.

I suppose it is.

In my particular case... I was married, we had a little girl, she was beautiful, they were both so beautiful.

But we had our problems. I wasn't the best husband, I was small-time. Still am. Set my sights too low for her, unnerstand?

Yeah, yeah.

And eventually... eventually she gets... it's not enough, right...?

I mean...

Hey man, you all right? Don't be too hard on yourself...

Yeah. Oh yeah. I'm sorry. I'm fine. I'm really sorry.

Hey, tha's okay. Why don' I buy you a cuppa coffee'r somethin'?

That'd be real kinda you.

Real kind.

30

How long were they together?

Eight years or eight months?

Oh shit. You drew an eight?

Gimme that.

Can't even force a draw anymore.

It was supposed to be a three... Got the suit right, anyway.

Three years. Which is what, the blink of an eye t'me, a century'r somethin' like that t'you.

To them...?

All I know is they were the best an' the worst thing that ever happened to each other.

I feel a lot of things... Relieved...

Scared?

Yeah.

I've never hit anyone in my life, Ernie.

I mean really *hit* someone. I didn't expect... I couldn't have guessed...

I mean, it hurt *me*. That anger was strong enough to break his nose, but it broke my hand, too.

And something else... my "contract with society," or whatever.

I broke the law.

There's actually a warrant out for my arrest. Can you believe it?

Jesus.

I'm sure the cops have better things to do than hunt down some angry girl, though.

Oh my God, this is just crazy.

It *is* crazy. Everything's different now.

I have nothing to go back to.

32

I shouldn't... Maybe I shouldn't even say it...

...but you can come back to me.

...

I know I know I know. That was stupid. I know better, I really do.

I just can't help thinking it, seeing you again.

It's okay. It's good to see you, too. To know you're all right.

Well, I'm homeless, and destitute, but I'm alive. That's something, I guess.

I haven't had a drink since Al showed up. Three weeks on the wagon.

What? What is it?

It's hard for me to look at you.

Why did they stop?

You expect me t'know the answer t'that? People are complicated, kid. No one really knows but them.

You know why your parents split up?

Mom wanted Dad to clean up his act.

Well, there's more to it than that, you can bet.

All sortsa things go on between people when they're close. Things that're hard t'say.

The words get all mixed up with the feelings.

shuff

Why would your mom leave you and your dad?

She must love you very much. She musta had a really good reason t'leave.

What reason could be that good?

Aw jeez, I dunno...

Pick a card?

This the place?

Yeah. See that symbol?

Compare it to the one on this card I got from the pawn shop.

They're similar, Ernie, but...

I'll just be a second. I'm just going to see if they have a member or an employee named Morton Crane.

What's going on?

You're askin' the wrong guy, sweetheart.

He wants to find whoever found the strait suit—

I mean, jacket.

36

 And what's he going to do when he finds this guy?

 I don't know. He's been, what do you call it —

 Obsessed.

 Obsessed with the idea ever since we visited that shop.

 Ernie...?

They've never heard of him.

 Why are you so — Ernie! Wait up, will you?

This don't look good.

38

Huh. That's a surprise. I wouldn't have guessed you remember every person you swindle.

Actually, I remember them best of all. Y'have to when ya work a limited area. Plus, you were ready t'kill me; tends t'make an impression.

'Course, you were better lookin' with alla yer hair...

Those men's overalls?

Are you trying to make a *point*, Mr. Lender?

Is my haircut, or my, my *clothing* some sort of reason you can't *apologize* for ripping me off ?!?

Uh, er... no... I...

It's just that, um...

I never, well...

I never had to do that before.

I'm sorry.

Ah, nourishment.

Sure am grateful for those extra groceries you bought, Esther.

Ernie.

Want some soup?

Say, y'know that coffee shop ya worked at?

The cash register...

I'm not hungry.

Was it one a them computerized numbers?

Why do you ask?

Just curious. Modernization tends t'affect my work.

Yeah, it was.

You know, credit cards, bank cards, phone codes, alla that electronic stuff...

Somehow I can't picture you working the technological angle.

Yeah, I hate that shit, but I gotta stay on toppa it, just the same.

40

I operate best when the cash *exists*, y'know?

Can't do anything with it when neither one of us can lay our hands on it.

Like cards, right, old man?

Where's the trick if you're watchin' it on T.V.?

I'm really tired. I think I'm going to turn in too.

Well don't you two go getting any ideas.

I got another hand to break if I need to, Mr. Lender.

Hey, all I'm sayin' is that there's children present, okay?

I'm just tryin' t'maintain a wholesome environment.

You okay?

41

No. No, she's not coming back.

Claire...

Why, Dad? Why?

Aw, honey...

Ssshh...

Why did she leave without me? WHY?

She didn't love me!

She did, honey. She loved you so much.

But why did she leave without at least trying to take me?

SHE DIDN'T WANT ME!

sniff

She did, sweetie.

She did want you.

I wouldn't let her take you.

Ernie!

Oh, shit.

Rmf!

AAAH!

Oh God, oh God...

TELL ME!

Ernie, *please*, I can't bear it, I—

Did you love him?

How can I possibly answer a question like that? No? Yes? What can I say to that? You know that I love *you*...

Howard and I hardly ever even spoke to each other!

Exactly!

So how can you know why he did it? I'm his brother, for Christ's sake, and *I* don't know!

I could see myself in him.

I... felt connected to him in this way that's inexplicable.

I felt like... like I just understood him.

48

And you didn't understand me?

I did, I *do* understand you.

But it's out of a *desire* to understand you.

It's the difference between what you're stuck with and what you want to have. Howard and I were stuck with the same thing.

And what was that?

I can't describe it. I think we experienced the world in the same way.

It was a weight...

I don't know. And that was reason enough.

"Enough," what's that?

It was a choice; that's all either of us can know for sure. You know how good he was, and how completely impossible that escape is. He knew what he was doing.

But that's not the choice I want to make. I just understand what brought him to it.

I'm tired.

Let's get you down.

whup!

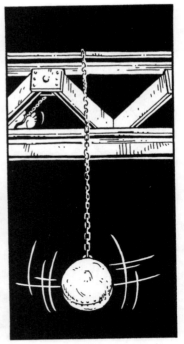

Ouch.

HA HA HA
HA HA HA
HA HA HA

Ha ha
ha ha

Where's
the key?

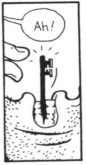

Ah!

CLICK

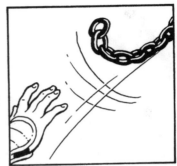

50

51

Mom?

Mommy—
Wait! Don't
leave!

Sixteen times
and the Queen
of Clover...

Wait a sec, wait
a sec, that's
not right...

What's
gone missin',
kiddo?

Ache up,
will ya?

Let's go, wake up!

C'mon, c'mon. Yer dad, too.

HEY! LENDER! UP AN'AT 'EM!

Huh? Whuzzat?

What's goin' on?

They're gone.

Ernie and Esther?

Whattaya wanna do about it?

I just wanted t'let ya know I was goin' t'look for 'em, okay? There's tracks off this way.

...

Uh—wait! Old man!

Hanh?

Y'got any lockpicks on ya?

Maybe I do, maybe I don't. Why?

I was, y'know, wonderin' if y'had one Claire could practice more with while you were gone.

I've only taught her a little cuz she asked. She's supposed t'be learnin' other stuff.

Yeah, I know, but uh... Jeez, look, it's not just for practice, okay?

Help me out here, will ya, Flosso? This just might be that Ace you were yappin' about.

I must be nuts t'actually buy that line from a con man.

Thanks.

Whatever yer up to, don't blow it.

What's going on? What do you need that pick for?

Things're lookin' up, pumpkin.

Get yourself dressed an' get that lock outta the glove box, there's a good girl.

We're goin' somewhere, an' you can practice on the way.

POUND! POUND POUND!

HEY! ANYONE IN THERE?!

POUND

Shit, Marty, gimme a hand up here, will ya?

Help me figure out what's wrong with this thing!

The fusebox is in the bathroom, you moron! Maybe a fuse blew or something!

Hey, whoa, chill out.

'Scuse me, pal.

Y'know? I don't have to take that kinda abuse...

CASHMASTER

'Specially in front of customers.

Hey. Hello?

I'm from Cashmaster, the register people? You gotta problem with yer unit?

Wow, that was fast. We didn't even call you yet!

Don't have to these days. Machine in my district goes down, signals my beeper, an' here I am. What's the scoop?

Uh, it's broke. Drawer's stuck.

The deuce, you say.

The what?

The deuce in these models is always overloadin'!

I got one out in the van. Unplug it for me back there, huh?

Uh, okay...

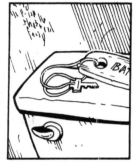

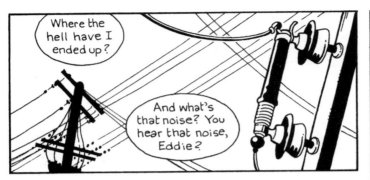

Where the hell have I ended up?

And what's that noise? You hear that noise, Eddie?

More of a feelin' than a noise. I can feel it in me.

Jesus *Christ*, it's givin' me th' creeps.

It's gettin' louder. In my bones an' gettin' louder by th' minute...

I gotta siddown, okay? I'm exhausted, I need a rest.

Where am I? I don't like this place.

It's like a fuckin' *nest*.

BANKB

That's exactly what it is, some kind of spider's nest.

An' I don' wanna be here when the owner comes home.

60

All night? What the hell were— Ah forget it, I don't wanna know.

As long as ya got ridda that straitjacket.

Ya *did* get ridda it, right?

Yeah. Dumped it in the river. Who knows where it'll end up.

Who cares. All that matters is it's gone.

Lender'll be upset, but he practically stole it anyway, so fuck 'im.

Ow! My feet are killing me!

Serves ya right, runnin' off without any shoes.

And in yer underwear, too! Lucky ya didn't freeze!

Hey, what—?

I can't get it, Dad. It's a different kind of lock.

Damn.

Maybe Al could pick it when he gets back.

Or, I guess you could just smash it open...

Shit.

NATHAN!

CLAIRE!

The police... are coming... We've got to... got to get a move on!

Up the dirt road.

I forgot what day it was.

We've got to hurry and get the car all loaded up.

C'mon, Dad!

Dad?

Yeah, pumpkin.

You start packin'

Uh, Esther...

I know gettin' outta town is high on yer lista priorities. Here're the keys to the car.

64

An' here's somethin' else...

What?

Claire's mom's address down south.

Please... I need you to take my daughter there.

DAD?!? What are you—?!

Now now, honey. It's about time you got to see your mom again.

C'mere an' say goodbye to your ol' Dad.

Wait wait wait— You tellin' me you got it fer Duffy?

Y'have t'say it like that? Like it's a virus'r something? Shit, it doesn't matter. What kinda chance've I got with her?

None. I fall all over myself around her but I might as well not exist.

But I mean... Duffy? She's so, jeez, I dunno, manly.

Yeah. I bet she can play poker.

She doesn't take anyone's shit —

And have you seen the way she holds a gun?

CRASH!

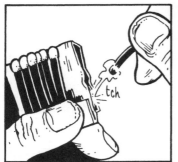

Nathan's getting himself caught to hold off the cops; Esther and Claire are —

Leaving.

Oh, is *that* all.

We'll see each other again.

I know we will.

Hey kiddo, hey... Yer dad knows what he's doin'?

He's doin' this cuz he loves you, okay?

He wants you to be able t'have a better life.

sniff

Okay, Al, we've got to go now. Say goodbye.

I am, I am.

Here, kiddo. I'm not gonna need this thing any-more.

It'll take awhile t'grow into it, and top hats ain't exactly ladies' wear, but I bet it'll look sharp on ya.

RRRRRMM